YOU'RE THE V...
Frank Sinatra

©International Music Publications Ltd
First published by International Music Publications Ltd in 2002
International Music Publications Ltd is a Faber Music company
3 Queen Square, London WC1N 3AU

Series Editor: Chris Harvey
Editorial, production and recording: Artemis Music Limited
Design: IMP Studio
Photography ©2002 Michael Ochs Archive / Redferns Music Picture Library
Printed in England by Caligraving Ltd
All rights reserved

ISBN10: 0-571-52871-6
EAN13: 978-0-571-52871-4

To buy Faber Music publications or to find out about the full range of titles available,
please contact your local music retailer or Faber Music sales enquiries:

Faber Music Ltd, Burnt Mill, Elizabeth Way, Harlow, CM20 2HX England
Tel: +44(0)1279 82 89 82
Fax: +44(0)1279 82 89 83
sales@fabermusic.com
fabermusic.com

RESPECT
THE VALUE OF
MUSIC

Frank Sinatra
Born 1915

Frank Sinatra's unmatched talent and remarkable voice set him aside as one of the 'all time greats' of twentieth century music. With a style that remained his own through over fifty years of change, Sinatra wowed the crowds from the swinging sixties right up until the resurgence in popularity of swing music in the nineties - a feat that has been surpassed by no-one.

The young Sinatra attended a Bing Crosby concert in 1933, and decided to pursue a music career after being moved by what he heard. Success shortly followed in the form of a radio talent program, in which Sinatra, along with the dancing trio the Three Flashes, won first prize as the Hoboken Four. This led to more performances with Major Bowes' travelling show, and regular spots on several radio stations. Sinatra soon joined Harry James's band, The Music Makers, as lead singer, but left after seven months to join Tommy Dorsey's swing orchestra. In 1943, whilst still with Dorsey, Sinatra released his first hit song *All or Nothing At All*, which had actually been recorded in 1939 whilst he was still with The Music makers. This song gave Sinatra a name for himself, and he bought out of Dorsey's contract to pursue a solo career.

The nineteen-fifties held some difficulties for Sinatra. In 1951 he left his first wife Nancy and their three children for the actress Ava Gardner, and in 1952 his singing career was nearly finished by severely damaged vocal chords. In the same year Sinatra was dropped by Universal, CBS-TV, Columbia Records and his agent. However, in 1953 Sinatra signed with Capitol Records and began rebuilding his career. Collaborations with arranger Nelson Riddle produced some of the most popular albums of the time, such as *Songs for Young Lovers*, *Come Fly With Me* and *In the Wee Small Hours*. In 1957 Sinatra's marriage to Ava Gardner ended in divorce. In the same year, the Rat Pack as we know it today was created under the leadership of Sinatra, and was made up of Dean martin, Sammy Davis Jr., Peter Lawford, and Joey Bishop.

Frank Sinatra formed his own record label - Reprise Records - in the sixties and he had number one albums with *Nice and Easy* and *Strangers in the Night*. In 1966 he married the actress Mia Farrow, who was thirty years his junior. They divorced in 1968 and in 1976 Sinatra married his fourth and final wife, Barbara Jane Blakely Marx, Zeppo Marx's widow. Sinatra announced his retirement from both recording and acting in 1971, but made a comeback two years later with the release of the television special and album *Ol' Blue Eyes is Back*. A national tour was conducted in 1990 to celebrate the star's seventy-fifth birthday, and his lifetime of musical accomplishments was recognised four years later at the Grammy Awards with the prestigious 'Legend' award.

Frank Sinatra died of a heart attack on May 14th, 1998 aged 82. The singer had been influential in almost six decades of sweeping changes in music, making nearly two thousand recordings and receiving nine Grammys. His unrivalled talent and popularity were illustrated by his final Grammy, awarded 47 years after his first record and stamping a seal on Sinatra being one of the most successful and valued performers of the twentieth century.

"The greatest singer in the history of popular music" (John Rockwell, music critic)

April In Paris

Words by E Y Harburg
Music by Vernon Duke

Backing

Come Rain Or Come Shine

Words by Johnny Mercer
Music by Harold Arlen

but I'm with you al - ways, I'm with you rain——— or——— shine.———

Fly Me To The Moon
(In Other Words)

Words and Music by Bart Howard

Backing

Medium swing

Fly me to the moon,— let me play— a - mong the stars,

let me see what spring is like on a - Ju - pi - ter and Mars. In

Fill my heart with song, — let me sing — for ev - er more, —

I've Got You Under My Skin

Words and Music by Cole Porter

The Lady Is A Tramp

Words by Lorenz Hart
Music by Richard Rodgers

Track 5
Backing

life with-out a care, she's broke but it's oke.

She loathes _____ Cal-i-for-nia, it's cold ___ and it's damp,

that's why _____ the la-dy, that is why the la-dy,

that's why la-dy ___ is a tramp. ___

My Kinda Town (Chicago Is)

Words by Sammy Cahn
Music by James Van Heusen

Track 6
Backing

My Way

French Words by Gilles Thibaut
English Words by Paul Anka
Music by Claude Francois and Jacques Revaux

Backing

Slow tempo

1. And now⎯ the end is near⎯ and so I face⎯ the fin-al cur-tain⎯ my friend,⎯ I'll say it clear,⎯ I'll state my case,⎯ of which I'm

(2.) -grets⎯ I've had a few⎯ but then a-gain⎯ too few to men-tion,⎯ I did what I had to do,⎯ and saw it through⎯ with-out ex-

(3.) loved⎯ I've laughed and cried⎯ I've had my fill⎯ my share of los-ing,⎯ and now⎯ as tears sub-side,⎯ I find it all⎯ so am-

Theme from *New York, New York*

Words by Fred Ebb
Music by John Kander

Backing

Someone To Watch Over Me

Words and Lyrics by George Gershwin and Ira Gershwin

Track 9
Backing

Something Stupid

Words and Music by Carson Parks

YOU'RE THE VOICE

8861A PV/CD

Casta Diva from Norma - Vissi D'arte from Tosca - Un Bel Di Vedremo from Madam Butterfly - Addio, Del Passato from La Traviata - J'ai Perdu Mon Eurydice from Orphee Et Eurydice - Les Tringles Des Sistres Tintaient from Carmen - Porgi Amor from Le Nozze Di Figaro - Ave Maria from Otello

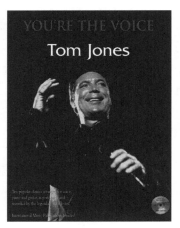

8860A PVG/CD

Delilah - Green Green Grass Of Home - Help Yourself - I'll Never Fall In Love Again - It's Not Unusual - Mama Told Me Not To Come - Sexbomb Thunderball - What's New Pussycat - You Can Leave Your Hat On

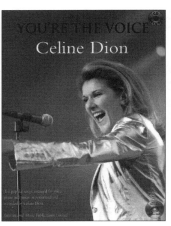

9297A PVG/CD

Beauty And The Beast - Because You Loved Me - Falling Into You - The First Time Ever I Saw Your Face - It's All Coming Back To Me Now - Misled - My Heart Will Go On - The Power Of Love - Think Twice - When I Fall In Love

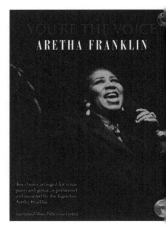

9349A PVG/CD

Chain Of Fools - A Deeper Love Do Right Woman, Do Right Man - I Knew You Were Waiting (For Me) - I Never Loved A Man (The Way I Loved You) I Say A Little Prayer - Respect - Think Who's Zooming Who - (You Make Me Feel Like) A Natural Woman

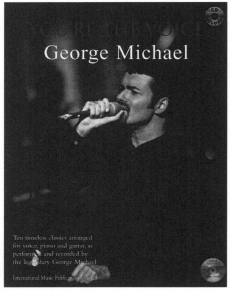

9007A PVG/CD

Careless Whisper - A Different Corner Faith - Father Figure - Freedom '90 I'm Your Man - I Knew You Were Waiting (For Me) - Jesus To A Child Older - Outside

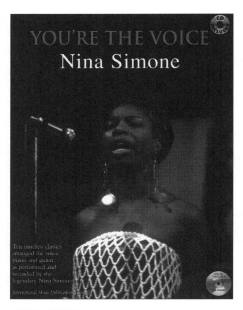

9606A PVG/CD

Don't Let Me Be Misunderstood - Feeling Good - I Loves You Porgy - I Put A Spell On You - Love Me Or Leave Me - Mood Indigo - My Baby Just Cares For Me Ne Me Quitte Pas (If You Go Away) - Nobody Knows You When You're Down And Out - Take Me To The Water

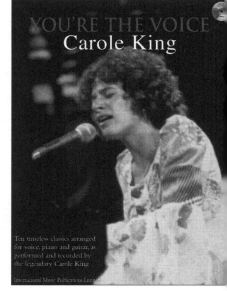

9700A PVG/CD

Beautiful - Crying In The Rain - I Feel The Earth Move - It's Too Late - (You Make Me Feel Like) A Natural Woma So Far Away - Way Over Yonder – Where You Lead - Will You Love Me Tomorrow You've Got A Friend

The outstanding vocal series from IMP

CD contains full backings for each song, professionally arranged to recreate the sounds of the original recording